Elsa's Style

A girl loves a special outfit for every occasion!

Read Elsa's story and dress your magnetic doll in the beautiful outfits. Fill in your activity pages, design and play.

Elsa Dress-Up Wardrobe

Dress up Elsa in her glittery gowns and accessories.

1. Snow Queen Gown

2. Coronation Gown

Elsa

Always In Style

A princess loves a new
gown for a special occasion!

3.
Spring
Gown

4.
Around
Town
Dress

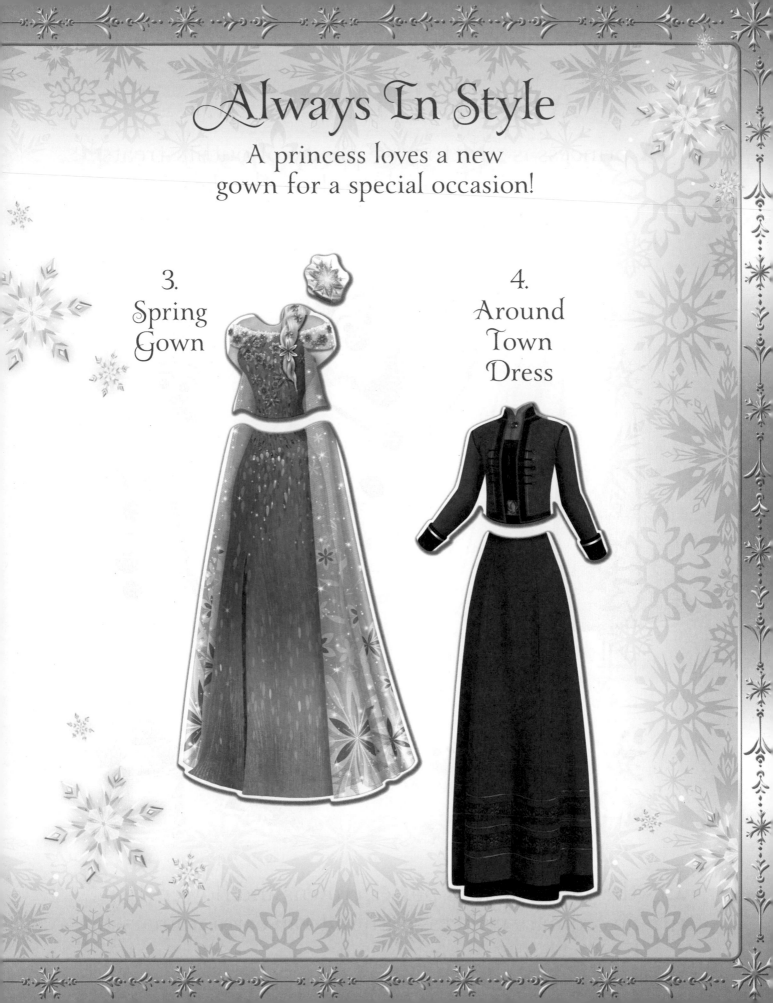

Around Town . . .

A princess is sure to have plenty of outfits, treats,
and special friends to share the day.

Olaf

It's the glittering fans, purses, crowns and flowers that
turn an ordinary princess outfit into an extraordinary one.

and More!

Create stories and adventures to go with
your new outfits and accessories.

My Favorite Gown

A snow queen with the magical powers to control ice and snow loves a stunning sparkling gown in the colors of ice blue and frosted silver. The gown sparkles and swishes as she creates ice sculptures in the air!

Dress Elsa in her stunning blue and silver gown!

My Ice & Snow Gown

Draw a picture of your beautiful icy gown.

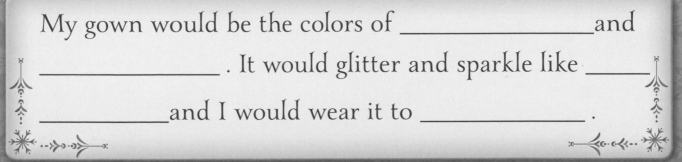

My gown would be the colors of _____ and
_____ . It would glitter and sparkle like _____
_____ and I would wear it to _____ .

Fill in your personal page.

Elsa the Queen

The townspeople of Arendelle were happy to have Elsa as their queen. On her coronation day she wore a beautiful blue gown with an embroidered bodice and a regal purple cape. A sparkling golden crown was placed on her head to make her the queen .

Dress Elsa in her coronation gown and crown.

A New Queen

This is Me!

The townspeople of

_____

will today announce their
new queen _____.

She has been chosen because she
will help care for our people by...

1._____

2._____

3._____

All rejoice, and join
in the celebration!

A New Spring Dress

It's Anna's Birthday, and Elsa is planning a big surprise party in the courtyard. Elsa grabbed some flowers from a vase and created a new outfit for herself. Her soft green dress is perfect for Anna's special birthday party!

Dress Elsa in her pretty spring dress.

My Spring Outfit

My favorite spring outfit is _____
_____

I like this outfit because it makes me feel_____
_____

I wear this _____
_____

Fill in your personal page. Draw or add a photo.

Around Town

Every girl loves a comfortable dress for walking through town, running errands, and shopping. A pretty blue outfit is perfect for visiting a bakery or book shop. A market is a great place to find hidden treasures!

Dress Elsa in her beautiful blue outfit.

The Best Places in Town

My favorite shop is _____

_____

If I could pick anything off the shelf it would be _____

_____

The best place to buy a snack is

_____

I always get _____

_____

_____

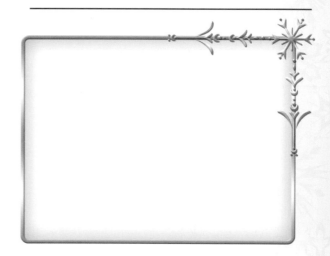

The place with the coolest toys is _____

_____

My favorite toy is _____

_____

Fill in your personal page. Draw or add photos.

Palace Party

Every girl loves to go to an evening party at the royal palace (even if she lives there)!

Draw Elsa in a new sparkling party gown!

A Royal Invitation

Dear Princess _____,

    You are cordially invited to the Royal Palace for a

_____ . This event shall be held on the

date of _____ at exactly_____

o'clock. The music will be performed by_____

_____ . The chef will be preparing a special treat

of _____ for the occasion. There will be

dancing and _____ throughout

the evening, and certainly a magical time for all!

    Sincerely yours,

_____

Winter Magic

Whether going out for
a sleigh ride, ice skating
or visiting friends,
a girl loves to
look dazzling.

Draw Elsa in a new glittering winter gown!

When the Weather Gets Chilly!

When the weather gets chilly I like to wear my _____ and _____ . I like to go outside to _____ _____and catch snowflakes on my tongue. Afterwards I cuddle up with my _____ in my toasty_____ and sip a cup of warm _____ by the fire. Sometimes I watch my favorite movie _____ _____or if I am with my friends we like to _____ and_____ .
Chilly days can be lots of fun!

My Own Royal Style

My Fashion Inspiration:

Add drawings, clippings, or photos of a favorite outfit.

My Favorite Colors:

Add drawings, swatches, or photos

Fill in your personal page. Add your own drawings or photos.

My Friends and Me

How We Met

My Friends

_____

_____

_____

_____

_____

_____

Things We Do Together

Fill in your personal page.

Family Forever

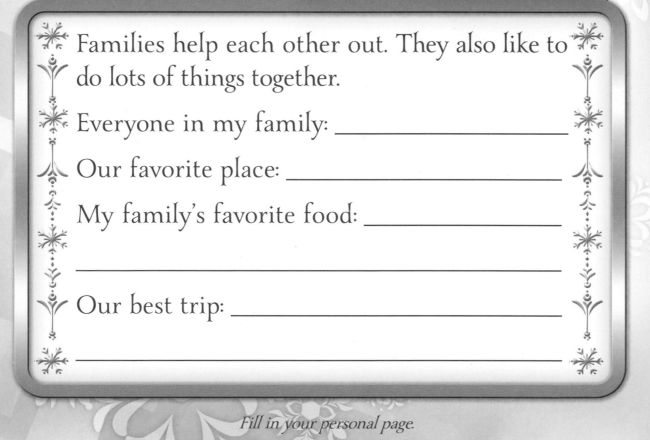

Draw or paste a picture of a special family member here.

Families help each other out. They also like to do lots of things together.

Everyone in my family: _____

Our favorite place: _____

My family's favorite food: _____

_____

Our best trip: _____

_____

A Dazzling Crown

Adorned with jewels and gems, a queen's crown sparkles
almost as much as her personality!

Make your crown shine! Coloe and decorate.

A New Hairstyle

A royal outfit is not complete without a fancy new hairstyle. It's fun to try braids, buns, or even special long curls! Sparkling tiaras, barrettes, or flowers can add the perfect accent to a new hairstyle.

Show off your hairstyle ideas. Design, color and decorate!

Fit For a Snow Queen

Every girl loves a new gown!

Design a new outfit for Elsa.

Spot the Difference!

A.

B.

C.

Circle the version of Anna that is different from the others.

Dressed For Adventure

A free-spirited adventurer like Anna needs a new outfit
made for exploring magical places.

Design a new outfit for Anna.

My Favorite Things

My Friends

Hobby: _____
_____
Sport: _____
_____
Movie: _____
_____
TV Show: _____
_____
Song: _____
_____
Book: _____
_____
Food: _____
_____

My Family

Fill in your personal page.

My Winter Outfit

Draw or paste a picture of your winter outfit here.

This outfit is so _____ and _____. I would wear this outfit to _____ or _____. My parents would probably _____ _____ when they saw me wearing it!

Snowflake Matching

Elsa has created two of each snowflake!
Help Elsa match each snowflake with its
double by drawing a line between each
set of identical snowflakes.

Winter Word Search

f	k	k	a	u	l	f	r
r	x	r	q	n	p	o	e
i	m	i	y	b	n	l	i
e	l	s	a	q	c	a	n
n	a	t	s	p	o	f	d
d	w	o	l	v	e	s	e
v	e	f	s	m	e	p	e
d	i	f	x	z	g	n	r

Can you find all the words above?

Friend	Anna
Kristoff	Sven
Elsa	Reindeer
Wolves	Olaf

How Many Snowflakes?

Snowflakes galore! Olaf is having so much fun in the falling snow. Can you help him count how many snowflakes are in the air?
There are _____ snowflakes.

Strong Bond, Strong Heart

1. Who is the snowman who wants to see summer? __ __ __ __
F   A   L   O

2. Who is the mountain man who prefers to be alone? __ __ __ __ __ __ __ __
T   O   S   K   F   I   R   F

3. Who is the sister of the Queen of Ice?

__ __ __ __
N   A   N   A

4. Who can make things from ice and snow?

__ __ __ __
A   S   E   L

5. Who is Kristoff's loyal reindeer friend?

__ __ __ __
N   E   V   S

Unscramble the words and write them in the spaces.

My Sparkling Snow Globe

If you could create anything inside the glittering and swirling snow globe, what would you make? Draw your own sparkling scene inside.

Sister Talk!

Sisters are like best friends, they are always there to talk with you, and sometimes sisters say the funniest things!

Fill in each oval with a silly phrase or sentence.

Crystal Snowflakes

Snowflakes come in all shapes and sizes. No two snowflakes are ever the same! They each have different points, sparkles, loops, and lines that make each one unique and beautiful to look at.

Design your own snowflake.

Palace Maze

Start

Finish

Anna loves to run through the many rooms of the palace. Help her find her way through the beautifully decorated hallways of the Arendelle palace.

Complete the maze to help Anna get through the palace. Color and decorate.

Friends Forever

Draw or paste a picture of your family and friends.

Snowman Friend

Building a snowman is so much fun!
If you had magic powers and could make
a snowman come to life, what would
your snowman look like?

Design your own snowman friend.

A Winter Tale

Now it's your turn to tell a story!

winter storm

wolves

glittering ice palace

snowman

wise troll

sparkling crystals

blast of ice

reindeer

snow

magical powers

exciting ending

spell

frozen heart

Arendell

secret

true love

ice-skating

northern lights

sisters

the North Mountain

suddenly

cliff

See if you can use all of phrases above to create your own winter story.